THE
CHINESE-AMERICAN
SONG AND GAME BOOK

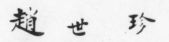

CHAO SHIH CHEN

THE
CHINESE-AMERICAN
SONG AND GAME BOOK

Compiled by

A. GERTRUDE JACOBS

Illustrations by CHAO SHIH CHEN
Music by VIRGINIA AND RICHARD MATHER
Text Romanization by CHING YI HSÜ
Chinese Characters by YÜN HSIA

A. S. BARNES AND COMPANY, INC.
NEW YORK

To
THE LITTLE CARP
Jane Ellen, Karl, Larry
Anne, John and Doc

Introduction

This book is a partial outgrowth of work in a Physical Education Class at Yenching University, Peiping, China, during the fall of 1940. The class, Tung Ho Nien, Chao Ching Hsin, Hung Ai Lien, Yü Ho Ti, Tan Mei Yo and Wu Pei Chi, started their practice teaching in the University's Elementary School, under my supervision. It was surprising to me, a newcomer to China, to find that Chinese children had few games of their own, nor did they seem to know any of our traditional singing games and play activities of the West. Surely, I thought, the Chinese children must have some kind of games and rhythmic stories which they learned during these years. The class seemed quite sure they had nothing of the kind except the shuttlecock game, and a few chants which the amah would say in a sing-song rhythmic cadence. They were exactly what I was looking for, and I was amused when the class said, almost in unison, "O, that, *everybody knows those.*" However, I told them they would be new to the American children.

We had just begun to work on the collecting of these rhymes, arranging them to Chinese folk tunes, and finding game elements for the words, when the United States government suggested Americans come home on the evacuation ships sent for them. Therefore, I had neither time nor opportunity to check the authenticity of the students' contributions and it is possible some of the material may have been handed in to fulfill a class assignment with little regard for the real purpose we had in mind. The contributions of Hung Ai Lien are perhaps the most authentic, as other Chinese friends in America say they have heard some of these rhymes in their childhood.*

Rushed though I was with sudden departure preparations, I felt I could not leave "The Garden of the Swallows" without asking Chao Shih Chen to do some illustrations for our so-called Chinese ditties. Miss Chao Shih Chen was a quiet, shy, fourteen year old girl who lived outside our gate in the Village. She supported her aging parents by making exquisite book marks of beautiful ladies in old pre-Manchu costumes and place cards of happy Chinese children which were sold at the Yenching book store and to the tourists in Peiping. Since the Chinese figures on this work were so very lovely, I was sure she could make some effective illustrations for the games.

It was very difficult to make her understand. She did not know a word of English, and, in Chinese, I could not cope with

---

*On checking the rhymes after my return to America, I find them all authentic and traditional folk ditties. The only one in the set which is not, is found in *Young Scholars*. This is a combination of two authentic Chinese rhymes which, unfortunately, I arranged myself. Surely, I thought, these rhymes can't be Chinese because they are so like the nursery rhymes we have in America.

8

much more than to identify myself, count to ten, tell time, and turn a rickshaw around. The cook, as usual, came to the rescue and with his help we were able to persuade Miss Chao Shih Chen to undertake the assignment. At first she was very reluctant, never having done any such work before, but finally she agreed to try. The next day she brought me several pen-and-ink sketches which were more than satisfactory. However, she was hesitant in showing me her one colored illustration. As soon as I saw that, I managed to say something like "hai yao i ke" many times ("I want another one"). She nodded she understood. Two days later she brought the set of pictures which you see in this book and asked the cook if she had interpreted my directions correctly. It is still difficult for me to believe that this is actually Chao Shih Chen's first work, yet those who knew her better say she had done very few pieces other than the work previously mentioned. If she could do this without having had instruction, what could she not do with instruction? Soon after that it was arranged that she go to art school in Peiping to study with a well-known Chinese artist. I anxiously awaited the completion of her next assignment, which was to be drawings illustrating happenings in the daily life of the Chinese child. My disappointment was great indeed when I opened the package brought to America by Gertrude and Ruth Hung and found Miss Chao's style had so completely changed. Her art instruction had begun to make itself felt. No longer did she include those lovely backgrounds surrounding the figures. Her teacher must have instructed her how a Chinese may paint figures as such, but without giving the human figure an equal or promi-

9

nent place in the landscape with nature. Man, in the Chinese mind, is assigned a very small and insignificant niche as his place in the Universe, and is usually so shown in painting. I have included two of her art school pictures here. They are The Bridal Chair and the Shuttlecock. She is no doubt working toward the principles governing the better Chinese artists, but I liked her first natural untrained expression better, perhaps because it is more familiar to the foreigner. Miss Chao was asked by the Yenching School of Religion to do some illustrations as soon as she had finished her art course. Soon after came December 7, 1941, and the doors of Yenching University were closed. Since then I have had no way of communicating with her to let her know that her pictures are now in book form for Western children to enjoy. Some day I hope to return to the village near the summer palace, the village of Manchu ex-royalty and Imperial bannermen, and see if I can find little Chao Shih Chen, who showed such promise in her first drawing.

The music was revised or written by Mr. and Mrs. Richard Mather of Berkeley, California, who fitted both the Chinese and American words into a Chinese-like melody, which Mr. Mather perhaps often heard as he was growing up in Paotingfu, China Mr. and Mrs. Mather also made many corrections and revisions throughout the manuscript.

Miss Ching Yi Hsü, a graduate student in the Education Department of the University of California, copied the Chinese characters and romanization which the Yenching students had handed in as their class work.

All of us who have worked on this book realize its many short-

10

comings, and are fully aware that it is not completely Chinese or American, but rather an attempt at the blending of the two cultures in this field. It is only what one person saw as an approach to a medium through which Chinese children could be introduced to their American playmates. Perhaps in the future I may have a better opportunity of furthering this exchange of friendship. If this book adds anything to the American child's understanding of the Chinese boy and girl I shall think it worthwhile to continue in this field.

I am very grateful to Josephine L. Rathbone, of Columbia University and to the Associated Board of Christian Colleges in China for making possible my own introduction to China through such persons as my Yenching students, my co-workers Ruth Chou, Martha Kramer, Lü Hui-Ching, K. A. Wee, Lin Chi Wu, Robert Chou, Margaret Speer, Dr. J. Leighton Stuart, Chih Pei Sha, and many others whose cooperation, kindness and courtesy are often called to mind.

I would also like to take this opportunity to thank Alice Nicholson Seacord for sketching the picture of Chao Shih Chen as I remembered her, Quail Hawkins for gently but firmly insisting I get the material ready for the publication of the book and also Dr. Yun Hsia for reading the manuscript, writing the Chinese brush characters, and helping me avoid some of the many errors which a foreigner so often makes in writing about things Chinese.

A. GERTRUDE JACOBS

翟　吉　如

11

Contents

THE
CHINESE=AMERICAN
SONG AND GAME BOOK

Baby's Playthings

Every Chinese doorway has a roof which serves as a shelter for the one about to enter. The door is divided into two parts which open either way. Usually a pair of antithetical couplets are painted or pasted on the door. The latter half of the following couplet appears on the door in the picture: "With faith and sincerity the family is preserved generation after generation, with writing and learning the word is passed on age after age." There is usually a wide board at the bottom of the doorway which one has to step over on entering. This is put there to keep the evil spirits out. At night the door is barred on the inside.

14

這是娃娃的喇叭　　嘟嘟嘟嘟吹
che shih wa wa ti la pa　　tu tu tu tu ch'ui

這是妹妹的鍵子　　隨着腳兒飛
che shih mei mei ti chien tzu　　sui che chiao erh fei

這是弟弟的空箏　　嗡嗡繩上鳴
che shih ti ti ti kung cheng　　weng weng sheng shang ming

這是娃娃的錘子　　叮噹叮噹叮
che shih wa wa ti ch'ui tzu　　ting tang ting tang ting

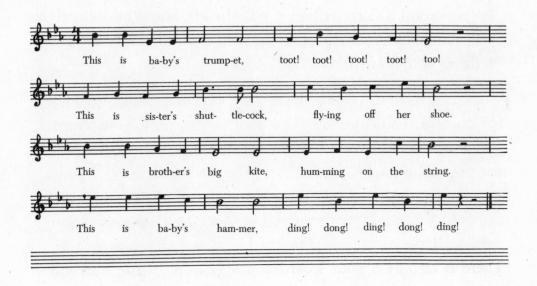

This is ba-by's trump-et, toot! toot! toot! toot! too!

This is sis-ter's shut-tle-cock, fly-ing off her shoe.

This is broth-er's big kite, hum-ming on the string.

This is ba-by's ham-mer, ding! dong! ding! dong! ding!

This is baby's trumpet, toot! toot! toot! toot! toot!
This is sister's shuttlecock flying off her shoe.
This is brother's big kite, humming on the string.
This is baby's hammer, ding! dong! ding! dong! ding!

Directions:

The children form a straight line with their chosen leader at the head of the line. The leader starts the game by marching forward blowing the horn. The followers imitate. The same is true of kicking the shuttlecock, flying the kite, and using the hammer.

Kite flying in China is an age-old activity for children; and beautiful kites in the shape of fish, butterflies, colorful dragons, bumble bees, huge paper birds, and animals are hung up at the fairs. These kites, mostly of paper, do not last very long but there is great sport as long as they are in the air. Sometimes the flyer will maneuver his kite to cross the cord of another kite and bring it down with his own.

A Tiger, A Leopard

The bridge in the background is somewhat like the picturesque camel back bridges which may be seen in the Summer Palace near Peiping. One reason for the high arch was to permit Imperial barges to pass through without taking down the masts.

Note the curve of the roof over the door. It is a popular belief in China that such a design keeps away the evil spirits. Because of the roofs being curved, the devil spirits slide off and are sent through the air in the opposite direction and therefore are not able to reach the ground.

18

The many sharp turns in the Chinese roads are often put there to foil the spirits, who, also being unable to turn corners, will continue on in the straight path and bump their heads on the stone tablet.

It is also for this reason that the roads in the rice fields wind around so much—that doors and windows are not placed opposite each other in the home—that spirit screens are placed before almost all entrances to Chinese homes and temples. The screens in front of the doors also give the courtyards more privacy as those passing along the street cannot see in.

一個虎, 一個豹,

yi　ke　hu　yi　ke　pao

一個按着. 一個跳.

yi　. ke　an　che　yi　ke　t'iao

A tiger, a leopard,
A tiger, a leopard,
One of them crouches,
The other jumps over.

Directions:

The children stand in two parallel lines, both lines facing the same direction. As they sing the "A tiger" the first line quickly squats down on knees with heads down in hands which are on the ground in front of them. As they sing "A leopard" the second line leaps up just behind the kneeling tigers. As they say "One of them crouches" the back line places hands on the backs of the kneeling tigers and jump over—running to a designated base ahead, and back to the home base before the tigers can catch them on the way back. The home base in this game is the steps in front of the door. If a leopard is caught, he must go to the tiger side. The game is repeated with the other side kneeling. The game continues indefinitely or until all of one side is caught. If, and when, this happens two leaders are chosen who choose sides for a new game.

To vary this game have just one from the front line be the tiger and only one from the back line be the leopard.

Little Bunny Rabbit

In this picture it is early spring. You will note the barren ground and the wisteria in the pine trees.

Animals in China have a very special place in the thinking of the people. Some Chinese believe that the soul may come back to earth after death in the form of an animal, or some other living thing.

The word Fu, meaning bat, has the same sound as blessing or happiness.

The Chinese, always ready for a play on words, use the emblem of the bat in many ways on various articles of clothing, paper decorations, etc.

(1) 兔兒，兔兒，請問為何你有大耳朵？

t'u erh t'u erh ch'ing wen wei ho ni yu ta erh to

為的聲音听得多，故有大耳朵。

wei ti sheng yin t'ing te to ku yu ta erh to

(2) 兔兒，兔兒，請問為何你有圓眼睛？

t'u erh t'u erh ch'ing wen wei ho ni yu yüan yen ching

為的東西看得清，故有圓眼睛。

wei ti tung hsi k'an te ch'ing ku yu yüan yen ching

(3) 兔兒，兔兒，請問為何你有三瓣嘴？

t'u erh t'u erh ch'ing wen wei ho ni yu san pan tsui

為的找食物便利，故有三瓣嘴。

wei ti chao shih wu pien li ku yu san pan tsui

(4) 兔兒，兔兒，請問為何你有四條腿？

t'u erh t'u erh ch'ing wen wei ho ni yu ssu t'iao t'ui

為的行路跑得快，故有四條腿。

wei ti hsing lu p'ao te k'uai ku yu ssu t'iao t'ui

(5) 兔兒，兔兒，請問為何你有短尾巴？

t'u erh t'u erh ch'ing wen wei ho ni yu tuan yi pa

為的行路不撥拉，故有短尾巴。

wei ti hsing lu pu po la ku yu tuan yi pa

23

1. Rabbit, rabbit, tell me, why do you have big ears?
   So I can hear more, that's why I have big ears.

2. Rabbit, rabbit, tell me, why do you have round eyes?
   So I can see better, that's why I have round eyes.

3. Rabbit, rabbit, tell me, why do you have three lips?
   So I can eat easier, that's why I have three lips.

4. Rabbit, rabbit, tell me why do you have four legs?
   So I can run faster, that's why I have four legs.

5. Rabbit, rabbit, tell me, why do you have a short tail?
   So it won't get in the way, that's why I have a short tail.

(Note the possible similarity to Little Red Riding Hood.)

Directions:

Single circle with partners facing. Number one is the rabbit and number two is the little boy who asks the questions.

The rabbit kneels, bends over as far as he can and puts his hands to the side of his head to indicate long ears. As the boy asks the questions, the rabbit responds with appropriate action. At the end of the game the boy and rabbit change places.

Goat, Goat, Jump Over the Wall

The grotesque shape of the rock in the foreground is probably due to its being allowed to weather under the action of water for many years before being brought into the garden.

During the Sung Dynasty (968-1280) the Emperor Hui Tsung, who, it is said, devoted more time to his painting than statecraft, built a famous rock garden in Kaifeng with stones from T'ai Lake. The effect he achieved by his ability to use rock as a means of expressing his ideas was copied by others for many generations. The porous rock quarried from the bottom of T'ai Lake became famous and often very high prices would be paid for authentic stones.

羊. 羊. 跳花牆.

yang   yang   t'iao   hua   ch'iang

抓把草. 喂你娘.

chua   pa   ts'ao   wei   ni   niang

你娘不在家.

ni   niang   pu   tsai   chia

喂你們老哥兒三.

wei   ni   men   lao   ke   erh   san

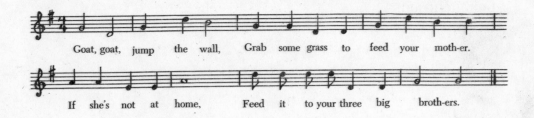

Goat, goat, jump the wall, Grab some grass to feed your moth-er.

If she's not at home, Feed it to your three big broth-ers.

Goat, goat, jump the wall,
Grab some grass to feed your mother.
If she's not at home
Feed it to your three big brothers.

Directions:

Form a single circle with hands joined to make a wall. The child in the center of the circle commands the "goat," who is on the outside of the circle, to "jump the wall." The goat does this as the children sing.

The object of the game is to grab a handful of grass or a pebble and give it to someone in the outer circle before the goat-herder in the center can catch or tag the goat. The goat-herder may give chase as soon as the goat has the grass in his hand, but not before. It may be necessary for the goat to run on the out-side of the circle to avoid being tagged by the goat-herder. When the goat has given the grass to his mother or three broth-ers, he may turn and chase the goat-herder. When the herder is caught the game begins again, a new goat and goat-herder being chosen.

Drum Hour

Here again is the walled courtyard which is the playground of so many Chinese children. Note the rice paper in the window, the reed matting which covers the door, the familiar tile roof, and the decoration under the eaves which the workman so quickly and easily designs.

It is an old Chinese custom to divide the 24 hours of the day into twelve units of two hours each. These are called "drum hours" and are still used by the night watchmen in Peiping, who make rounds every two hours beating out an intricate and dif-

30

ferent rhythm each time they pass your wall. This not only tells you the time in the dead of the night—that is, if you have familiarized yourself with the rhythms of each round—but it also serves the purpose of warning petty thieves and prowlers who may be about at that hour.

The old drum tower used in the days of Kublai Khan to warn the city of an enemy's approach, is said by some persons to be the one still standing in Peiping today.

THE 12 HORARY CHARACTERS
AND THE CORRESPONDING ANIMALS

Characters		Animals	Zodiac	Hours
子	tzu	鼠 Rat	Aries	11-1 a.m.
丑	ch'ou	牛 Ox	Taurus	1-3
寅	yin	虎 Tiger	Gemini	3-5
卯	mao	兔 Hare	Cancer	5-7
辰	ch'en	龍 Dragon	Leo	7-9
巳	szu	蛇 Serpent	Virgo	9-11
午	wu	馬 Horse	Libra	11-1 p.m.
未	wei	羊 Sheep	Scorpio	1-3
申	shen	猴 Monkey	Sagittarius	3-5
酉	yu	鷄 Cock	Capricornus	5-7
戌	hsü	狗 Dog	Aquarius	7-9
亥	hai	猪 Boar	Pisces	9-11

The months of the year and the cycle of years are called after animals, and when the series and the various orderly combinations have been used, the cycle starts over again at the end of sixty years.

In this game are combined the drum hours and the names of the animals in the cycle.

At the first drum hour oh, the rat is stealing rice.
At the second drum hour oh, the ox pulls the plough.
At the third drum hour oh, the tiger jumps the log.
At the fourth drum hour oh, the hare hops to his friend.
At the fifth drum hour oh, the dragon rides the clouds.
At the sixth drum hour oh, the snake crawls on the ground.
At the seventh drum hour oh, the horse runs far away.
At the eighth drum hour oh, the sheep drinks at the brook.
At the ninth drum hour oh, the monkey climbs the bamboo.
At the tenth drum hour oh, the cock crows in the morning.
At the eleventh drum hour oh, the dog runs to his master.
At the twelfth drum hour oh, the boar goes under the fence.

Directions:

A single circle with hands joined. The rat is in the center.
All sing the first line while the rat nibbles the rice.
The rat stands in front of someone while the group claps.
The whole group imitates the two rats.
At the beginning of the second line the above two go into the center as oxen and the game is repeated.
At the beginning of the third line four go into the center as tigers, etc.

32

During the last line all in the circle join hands,—stoop down and try to keep the boars from going under fence.

The game is repeated with a new rat.

If the group is small the leader can take one new one into the circle each time during each verse and let the others stay in the center and act out the actions of the various animals. Let each child feel free to do his or her own interpretations of the game.

Flowers Through the Moon Gate

The moon gate in the picture is often found in Chinese gardens. Besides making the numerous courtyards more accessible to the ever increasing family, the moon gate often serves as a frame for a beautiful vista.

The Chinese garden has been said to be "the cradle of freedom for the spirit" where one goes to seek solitude, meditation, and inspiration. It is an intimate expression of a Chinese philosophy of life and for that reason is to be enjoyed and lived in.

34

The gardens give the impression of great naturalness although much thought and care are put into the quaint rockeries, the informal winding streams, and the surprising vistas at every turn.

The willow tree symbolizes grace and friendship. Departing guests are sometimes given branches from the willow.

澆花，澆花，澆花難．
chiao hua   chiao hua   chiao hua nan

你不澆花，花就死．
ni   pu   chiao   hua   hua   chiu   ssu

一盆水，一壺茶，
yi   p'en   shui   yi   hu   ch'a

澆好水，開好花
chiao   hao   shui   k'ai   hao   hua

一盆水，二盆水．
yi   p'en   shui   erh   p'en   shui

好花開，開的大．
hao   hua   k'ai   k'ai   ti   ta

35

Sprinkle, sprinkle, sprinkle the flowers.
If you don't, then they will die.
One pan of water, one pot of tea.
Sprinkle them well to grow fine flowers.
One pan of water, one pot of tea.
Fine flowers grow and grow quite high.

Directions:

The children, squatting on the ground, sit in a circle. The one who has been chosen to be the flower sprinkler is on the outside of the circle carrying a wet cloth or a small pitcher.

The children sing the words as the sprinkler runs around the circle. On the word "high" he sprinkles water on the head of a kneeling child who rises up quickly and chases the sprinkler who tries to get back to the "sprinkled flower's" place before being caught. If so, the "sprinkled flower" now becomes the sprinkler.

36

Roses for Coppers

Chinese houses are usually surrounded by solid plastered brick walls which separate the houses from each other and from the streets.

The verandas extend in front of the house facing the entrance and are usually floored with smooth square brick. The many designed railings and pillars of Chinese homes are made of wood and painted with red lacquer.

The tree is probably a peach, whose blossoms symbolize Spring in Chinese paintings. Many of the flowers and trees have

38

symbolic meaning. The Plum, for instance, symbolizes brother-hood and friendliness and is the Chinese national flower. The Orchid, "a favorite of Kings" symbolizes culture, refinement and nobility of character; the Lotus truth and purity; the Magnolia, fragrance of virtue; and the Peony is considered "The King of Flowers."

1. 玫瑰花，玫瑰花，誰要買我的玫瑰花？

mei kuei hua   mei kuei hua   shui yao mai wo ti   mei kuei hua

2. 玫瑰花，玫瑰花，幾個銅錢一朵花？

mei kuei hua   mei kuei hua   chi ke t'ung ch'ien yi to hua

3. 不二價，不二價，兩個銅錢一朵花。

pu erh chia   pu erh chia   liang ke t'ung ch'ien yi to hua

4. 我要買，我要買，幾個銅錢兩朵花？

wo yao mai   wo yao mai   chi ke t'ung ch'ien liang to hua

5. 玫瑰花何時開？玫瑰花，何時開？

mei kuei hua ho shih k'ai   mei kuei hua ho shih k'ai

6. 玫瑰花，春天開，玫瑰花春天開

mei huei hua ch'un t'ien kai mei kuei hua ch'un t'ien kai

1. Red, red roses, red, red roses, who wants to buy my red, red roses?

2. Red, red roses, red, red roses, how many coppers for a bunch?

3. Just one price, just one price, just two coppers for a bunch.

4. I want to buy, I want to buy, how many coppers for two bunches?

5. Red, red roses, when do they bloom? Red, red roses, when do they bloom?

6. Red, red roses bloom in the spring. Red, red roses bloom in the spring.

Directions:

Hands are joined in a single circle. The flower seller is outside the circle with a basket of flowers. As the first line is sung the flower seller enters the circle: he stops in the center as line two is sung: as the third line is sung he walks around the circle and stops before some who says, "I want to buy." When asked how many coppers for two flowers the seller must be able to state the correct answer or he cannot sell the flowers. The number of flowers and the price can change with each new game. If the seller is able to answer the correct price for the number of flowers the purchaser wishes to buy, he may change places with the one who bought the flowers. The children all skip around in the circle as they sing "Red, red roses, when do they bloom, etc." They continue skipping until the question is answered by the group. The game begins over again with the new flower seller.

A Lion Comes

Only one family lives in the house across the river, as indicated by its construction. Chinese houses are usually built on three sides of a square courtyard. Great care is given as to location, direction, size and elevation. There is a set of superstitious building principles which have been followed since before the time of Confucius.

The child at the end might be called Little Carp (which grows up to be a dragon) and the others: Peach Fuzz, Little

Vegetable Dish, Thunderbolt, Iron Pillar, or even Little Tiger. The Tiger has great protective powers as well as devil-dispelling qualities, so quite often the children are seen wearing tiger shoes or caps.

楊 樹 葉 子 華 啦 啦.
yang　shu　yeh　tzu　hua　la　la

小 孩 睡 覺 找 他 媽.
hsiao　hai　shui　chiao　chao　t'a　ma

狼 來 啦, 虎 來 啦.
lang　lai　la　hu　lai　la

獅 子 來 啦, 我 打 他。
shih　tzu　lai　la　wo　ta　t'a

Pop- lar leaves go hua - la - la; Ba- by's sleep-y, wants ma-ma.

Here comes a wolf; here comes a ti-ger; Here comes a li-on; I'll chase him!

Poplar leaves go hua-la-la;
Baby's sleepy, wants mama.
Here comes a wolf, here comes a tiger,
Here comes a lion, I'll chase him!

Directions:

The children form a single line with their arms around the waist of the one in front of them. An odd player, the lion, stands in front of the group not closer than a designated spot.

As the children sing lines one and two they sway back and forth. As they begin to sing the third line the odd player out in front can now come off his confining territory and try to tag the last player in the line. The group is moved about by the front player in the line who keeps turning his line so that the last person cannot be tagged. This continues until the players sing "I'll chase him." Now the first player in the line tries to catch the "lion" before the "lion" can touch the last player in the line. As soon as the "lion" is caught he goes to the end of the line, and the person who was chasing him becomes the "lion." If the "lion" can touch the end of the line before the words "I'll chase him" are sung, then the game begins over again and he can still be the "lion" while the first person in the line has to be demoted to the end of the line.

Young Scholars

For centuries the Chinese children have been taught in small groups, or by tutors who hear them recite their lessons. It is very important that Chinese children study aloud in order that they get the proper sound or tone for each word.*

---

*I found trying to conduct part of a hygiene class in Chinese was a never ending source of amusement to the students. I had great difficulty in distinguishing differences among the four tones of a syllable. Since each tone or inflection could mean an entirely different word, I found myself, for instance, asking the students to "please be seated on the soap." There was no limit to these funny errors.

Likewise a great amount of time is spent in learning to write characters. Since there is no alphabet in Chinese, each character is something like a picture and many of these pictures put in their proper order expresses a thought.

The school name referred to in the game is a name given to a child as he starts school. He no longer uses his milk or baby name. As he grows into adulthood, he may take an official name, or, if he becomes a literary man he may assume a literary or pen name. His common surname, which is always written first, is kept throughout his life and for generations to come. If a three character name, the second and third character may be the child's own individual and personal name. In some families one of these characters is common and may be decided upon in advance for several generations, so that when one meets a new relative, it is easy to tell where he belongs in the generations of that family.

The village dogs bark at the crowing cocks. The window paper turns white.

From over the wall come the cries of the early morning peddlers.

Quickly we rise to prepare for school.

We say good morning to our parents and have breakfast.

We wrap our books in a square piece of blue cloth, with a cash tied in one corner to hold them securely.

We put our brass ink boxes, stone ink wells and our brush pens in our book bag and hurry away.

We tell our playmates our new schoolname.

We bow low to the portrait of Confucius, we bow to our teacher and quietly wait.

Directions:

The children form a single line, with one chosen as a leader. They pretend to be asleep until the cock crows. The leader chosen dramatizes, as he chooses, the getting up and going to school—the others imitate his actions.

Topsy-Turvy

The bamboo is a favorite of scholars and artists. It symbolizes gentleness, wisdom, and constancy. It also symbolizes an upright gentleman who can withstand the cold north winds of winter; it will bend but never break. The older it grows the stronger it becomes. The bamboo is also frequently used as an art motif.

The Chinese roof is tile, laid with mud over straw matting. Since the tile collects seeds and dust, it is not uncommon for

50

grass and other vegetation to grow on the roof. This causes the roof to disintegrate and often fall apart. The Imperial roofs were always yellow.

The game of Topsy-Turvy is a good example of the Chinese sense of fun. A Chinese Monk's head is shaven, so it is as absurd to catch him by the hair as for the deaf man to hear, etc. It was the Chinese sense of humor which made me feel more at home than anything else during my short stay in a country whose language I did not understand. The impact of a civilization, so different, was greater than I had anticipated. I was much less homesick when I discovered we both laughed at the same places in the Punch & Judy show or at the same tricks of the trained birds at the fair. I was also grateful to the Chinese babies who cried in a language which I could understand.

月亮白光光，

yueh liang pai kuang kuang

賊來偷醬鋼.

tsei   lai t'ou chiang kang

聾子聽見忙起牀.

lung   tzu   t'ing chien mang ch'i ch'uang

啞子高聲喊厨房.

ya   tzu   kao sheng han ch'u fang

51

跛子追上去.
po tzu chui shang ch'ü

瞎子也來幫.
hsia tzu yeh lai pang

一把抓住頭髮,
yi pa chua chu t'ou fa

看見是個和尚.
k'an chien shih ke ho shang

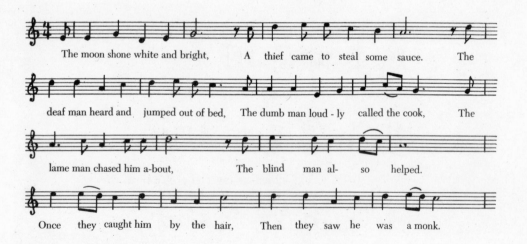

The moon shone white and bright,   A thief came to steal some sauce. The

deaf man heard and jumped out of bed, The dumb man loud-ly called the cook, The

lame man chased him a-bout,   The blind man al- so helped.

Once they caught him by the hair, Then they saw he was a monk.

The moon shone white and bright,
A thief came to steal some sauce.
The deaf man heard and jumped out of bed,
The dumb man loudly called the cook,
The lame man chased him about,
The blind man also helped.
Once they caught him by the hair,
Then they saw he was a monk.

Directions:

Each child in the circle chooses which one of the characters he will represent. On the first sentence they skip around. Then the thief goes through the center of the circle and out on the opposite side. As the song is sung the characters in turn start to chase the thief. The first one who can grab the thief by the hair is the one to start the next game.

The Grasshopper

The pine tree, a symbol of robustness, majesty, dignity and strength of character, stays green the year round, and does not shed its needles. It has been compared to an old man who knows how to grow old gracefully. On the countryside in North China, around Peiping, there are very few unguarded trees of any description. They have all been cut down for firewood. However, there is almost always a grove of trees surrounding temples and ancestral tombs. In Manchuria and South West China there are dense forests.

54

During the winter season the weather is rather cold in Pei-ping but with comparatively little snow. However, there is skating from about the middle of December until the latter part of February. In the spring the high winds bring dust from the Gobi desert, which gets into each nook and corner in the house and covers everything.

一 場 秋 風，一 場 凉，

yi　ch'ang　ch'iu　feng　yi　ch'ang　liang

一 場 白 露，一 場 霜，

yi　ch'ang　pai　lu　yi　ch'ang　shuang

嚴 霜 單 打 獨 根 草，

yen　shuang　tan　ta　tu　ken　ts'ao

螞 蚱 死 在 草 根 上.

ma　cha　ssu　tsai　ts'ao　ken　shang

A gust of Fall wind, blowing cold;
A fall of white dew, turned to frost.
The cruel frost freezes each blade of grass,
And the grasshopper dies in his grassy nest.

Directions:

A double circle with partners facing each other. Swing both arms, for the blowing wind. Cross the hands over the chest and bend over to indicate the cold. Reach up high, fall to the ground and hide head in the folded arms, indicating the grasshopper.

Peacock Feather

The carving on the top of such posts is frequently of small, playful lion cubs, each of which would be in a different position and each would have a different expression on its face. Beyond the carved marble balustrade may be a lake.

The tree is a weeping willow which is so common in North China gardens.

孔　雀　毛　　穿　桃　李

k'ung　ch'uan　mao　　ch'uan　t'ao　li

你　追　我　　我　追　你

ni　chui　wo　　wo　chui　ni

Peacock feather on a plum limb,
You catch me and I'll catch him.

Directions:

Form single circle with two blindfolded children in the center who try to catch each other as the ones in outer circle walk around singing the above words.

When one person is caught, the game ends; and the children who were in the center choose two more to take their places.

The game can be varied by having all the children kneel down at the beginning of the game, close their eyes, and put their heads in their folded arms. The leader chooses two children, who are blindfolded and put in the center. The game begins with the two blindfolded children trying to catch one another. After catching his opponent and identifying him correctly, the child may help the teacher choose the next two who are to start the new game.

59

Turned Cake

The frame of the window is usually painted with red lacquer. White rice or silk paper is pasted inside the frame. This paper is very strong and cannot easily be torn by wind and rain.

A railing is usually placed along the river or pond. It is not meant to be a wall. The trees are often tied in various designs when they are very young so that interesting shapes will develop as the tree grows older.

The children around Peiping often use the 'Yellow Earth' which has very great adhesive qualities for clay modeling. This clay earth is also used for very fine pottery, hence it is a favorite of the children.

It is the same kind of clay that, mixed with coal dust, is used in making coal balls, which many of the Chinese have to depend upon for heat in the cold winter months.

fan ping lao ping yu cha hsien ping

chi liu ku lu yi ke

Turned cake, pancake, deep-fried filled cake,
Hasty-pasty—here's one!

Directions:

A couple faces one another with hands joined. When they sing "Turned cake, pancake, deep-fried filled cake" they swing hands to and fro. When they sing "Hasty-pasty—here's one!" they raise arms high and turn under their own arms (one under his right, the other under his left). Then the game begins again.

A Happy Family

The tung oil which is used for waterproofing comes from this tung tree. This oil poured into baskets makes a good waterproof lining.

The paving stones of the courtyard are often broken tile, paving chips or small stones. The pattern is usually symmetrical with simple combinations.

The garden and courtyard walls are usually whitewashed, or colored a deep red, either of which makes an attractive back ground for flowers.

The rhyme for this game reminds one a bit of the "crooked man" of nursery fame.

鑼鍋老頭出門，一步，一步慢慢走。

lo　kuo　lao　t'ou　ch'u　men,　yi　pu　yi　pu　man　man　tsou

拾兩個大銅錢，插在耳上，背着手。

shih　liang　ke　ta　t'ung　ch'ien　　ch'a　tsai　erh　shang　pei　che　shou

半路遇見花貓，腿瘸不能爬高。

pan　lu　yü　chien　hua　mao　t'ui　ch'üeh　pu　neng　p'a　kao

耗子朋友又沒牙。他們都住在一家。

hao　tzu　p'eng　yu　yu　mei　ya　　t'a　men　tou　chu　tsai　yi　chia

The humpbacked old man goes out
Stepping, stepping, oh so slow.
He picks up two big coins,
Sticks them in his ear, folds his hands at his back.
He meets a cat on the way
Who is lame and cannot climb.
Another friend is a toothless mouse,
So they all three live in one house.

Directions:

The children form a single circle and divide up into old men, crippled cats and toothless mice. They break up and go to different sections of the play space. First the old men start out bent over and walking slowly. They bend to pick up the copper coins, pass the limping cats who are taken into the group, as are the toothless mice a little farther on. On a given signal the leader of the old men shouts what he has chosen for "home" and all run there to see who can first reach the spot.

64

Brother Chang

This seems to be the season of chrysanthemums which bloom so abundantly in Peiping during the fall and long into the winter. In the much used Chinese almanac there is a calendar which shows when the many flower festivals are held. The Chinese are a flower-loving people and often cultivate beautiful gardens of rare varieties.

The doorways are often of different shapes. The Chinese words for vase and peace sound the same, hence the symbol

66

of a vase-shaped doorway means, "May peace be with you in your coming in, and in your going out."

The two little boys on the end look as though they have put on their padded winter garments. Sometimes they wear so many that it is difficult for them to get up once they fall down.

張 大 哥, 費 大 哥,
chang   ta   ke   fei   ta˙   ke

出 門 碰 見 朋 友 多.
ch'u   men   p'eng   chien   p'eng   yu   to

你 拍 拍 手, 我 唱 歌.
ni   p'ai   p'ai   shou   wo   ch'ang   ke

有 飯 大 家 吃, 有 酒 大 家 喝.
yu   fan   ta   chia   ch'ih   yu   chiu   ta   chia   ho

大 家 快 快 樂 樂, 哈! 哈! 哈!
ta   chia   k'uai   k'uai   lo   lo   Ha   Ha   Ha

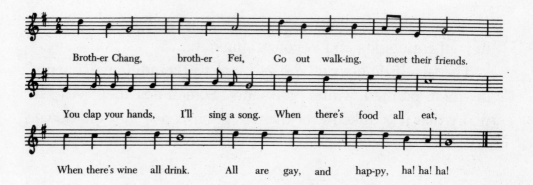

Broth-er Chang, broth-er Fei, Go out walk-ing, meet their friends.

You clap your hands, I'll sing a song. When there's food all eat,

When there's wine all drink. All are gay, and hap-py, ha! ha! ha!

Brother Chang, brother Fei
Go out walking, meet their friends.
You clap your hands, I'll sing a song.
When there's food all eat
When there's wine all drink.
All are gay and happy, ha! ha! ha!

Directions:

The children stand in two vertical lines facing one another. As they sing the first and second lines of the verse, both lines skip to the middle and bow to the opposite child and clap hands. He then joins hands with his opposite playmate, follows the leader and skips around in a double circle. As the last line is sung the child skips back to place and laughs.

68

Locust Tree

The balustrade is of carved marble with many designs. The figure on the post with the lotus shaped base is either a lion or a dog. It is a traditional and common practice to put two large lions on either side of an entrance. One lion often has a ball in its claw and the other is frequently carved playing with a cub under her paw. There is an interesting legend about this mother lion who is playing with her cub and feeding it through her paw.

The moon gate may be leading to another garden or courtyard, but not to the street. Here again is a picturesque rock.

70

槐　樹　槐　　槐　樹　槐，
huai　shu　huai　　huai　shu　huai

槐　樹　底　下　搭　戲　台.
huai　shu　ti　hsia　ta　hsi　t'ai

你　也　來，我　也　來，
ni　yeh　lai　wo　yeh　lai

我　家　的　姑　娘　還　沒　來.
wo　chia　ti　ku　niang　hai　mei　lai

說　着　說　着　就　來　了.
shuo　che　shuo　che　chiu　lai　la

騎　着　驢，打　着　傘.
ch'i　che　lü　ta　che　san

光　着　脚　兒，挽　着　鑽.
kuang　che　chiao　erh　wan　che　tsuan

Locust tree, locust, locust tree, locust,
Under the locust a stage is set.
You come along, I'll come too.
Our family's daughter is not here yet.
As we are talking, here she comes,
Riding a donkey, umbrella in hand,
Both feet bare, and a knot in her hair.*

*This line is slightly changed from the original.

This is perhaps an authentic folk rhyme referring to a country wedding. It may be a wedding where the bride is not able to have the chair bearers and all the presents and trousseau.

Directions:

Form a double circle with partners facing. Elbows bent in front of chest with the palms facing the chest.

As the words are said the children clap hands on each syllable in this manner.

Line 1. Slap own chest, clap own hands together, clap partners hands.

Slap own chest, clap own hands together, clap partners hands.

Line 2. Repeat the above three times.

Line 3. Slap partners right hand, slap partners left hand. Repeat three times.

Line 4. Clap partners hands ten times.

Line 5. Clap own hands together—partners right, own together, partners left. Repeat ending with hands together.

Line 6. Hook right arms with left held high above head and skip with partner one complete circle. When back in place drop hands.

Line 7. Repeat hooking left arms with right hand held back of the head.

72

The Bride's Chair Comes

Sometimes the parents dress their little sons in girls' clothing, arrange their hair like that of a girl, and say, "She's a worthless one, no spirit would want her."

In China it is very important that one have sons to carry on the family name, to worship at the ancestral tablets, and take care of the ancestral graves. It is considered unfilial to allow a family to die out and if there is only one precious son in the family, one may be assured everything is done to protect him from harm and the demon spirits.

74

上姑盧台，下姑盧台．張家的老媽倒茶來．
shang ku lu t'ai　hsia ku lu t'ai　chang chia ti lao ma tao ch'a lai

茶也香，酒也香．十八個駱駝駝衣裳．
ch'a yeh hsiang chiu yeh hsiang　shih pa ke lo t'o t'o yi shang

駝不動，叫馬勒．
t'o pu tung chiao ma lei

馬勒，馬勒噴口水．噴在小姐花褲腿．
ma lei ma lei p'en k'ou shui　p'en tsai hsiao chieh hua k'u t'ui

小姐，小姐，你別惱．明兒個，後兒個，車來到
hsiao chieh hsiao chieh ni pieh nao　ming-erh ke　hou-erh ke　ch'e lai tao

什麼車？紅軲轆轎車白馬拉．
shen ma che hung ku-lu chiao ch'e pai ma la

裡頭生着個巧人家．
li t'ou tso che ke ch'iao jen chia

灰鼠的皮襖．銀鼠褂
hui shu ti p'i ao　yin shu kua

一對兒荷包小針兒扎
yi tui-erh ho pao hsiao chen-erh ch'a

煙袋桿兒一尺八
yen tai kan erh yi ch'ih pa

75

Roll up the stage, roll down the stage,
The Chang family maid has come to pour tea,
Tea that is fragrant, wine that is sweet.
Eighteen camels carry the clothes.
They're too heavy, call in the horse.
The horse pulls, the horse pulls, and froths at the mouth.
He froths on my lady's flowered trousers.
My lady, my lady, don't you be cross.
Tomorrow or the next day the cart will come.
What cart is that? A red-wheeled sedan-cart drawn by white
   horses.
Inside is sitting a lucky fellow,
In an ermine coat and a squirrel gown.
A pair of sachets embroidered fine.
Tobacco pouch and pipe a foot or so long.

   The above chant of the amah refers to the wedding of the
lady in the embroidered trousers.

Directions:

   The children form a straight line after they have decided
which character they want to be in the above story. While they
are saying the first line they all stoop down and then rise on tip
toes pretending to prepare an imaginary stage. This stage perhaps refers to one of the mat sheds or awnings which is perhaps
being put up for one of the bride's parties. After the first line,
the children then act out the parts of the various characters
which they have chosen while the others continue to chant the
rhyme.

76

A wedding in China is a very colorful affair. It calls for a long period of preparation before the event, and, when the ceremony takes place, the festivities last far into the night. The necromancer has to be consulted about a number of things before the "go-between" can go ahead with his plans in arranging the marriage. In the first place, are the parties of the same surname? There are few more than four hundred different family names in China, and if the bride and groom happen to have the same family name the marriage cannot be arranged so easily. Are their birthdays in the proper year? If the bride was born in the cycle of the Tiger and the groom in the cycle of the Rabbit, the marriage should not be consumated, as the Tiger could eat the Rabbit and the marriage would not be a happy one.

With these, and many other limiting details out of the way, the necromancer seeks to find an auspicious day in the almanac when the event can take place. This almanac is a book, published every year, listing the days which are auspicious for various occasions, and is constantly referred to by many.

When the wedding day is finally settled, the mother of the groom sends presents to the bride. Invitations are sent out on red paper and the bride is prepared to leave the home of her ancestors. There is great lamentation in the bride's family as the day of her departure draws nearer. After marriage the daughter belongs to the family of her husband.

The procession starts out with great fanfare and colorful banners carried in front. Then follows the lantern bearers with the groom's name written on one, and the bride's family name written on the other. The lantern with the bride's name is often sent back to her home at the half-way mark. This, so it is said, was symbolic of the earlier days when the bride's family gave up the chase for a daughter who had been carried off by a tribe.

By observation I have never been able to discover if the long horns and the wood-wind instruments issuing the weird sounds had any relationship to Chinese music. All the processions I ever saw gave me the impression the musicians were tooting and blowing whenever they pleased.

78

Frequently, in Peiping, an ultra-modern bridal procession is preceded by a Western uniformed band or two. If so, one might hear something resembling "Ah Sweet Mystery of Life" and "Maine Stein Song" by the two different bands at the same time. Keeping in tune seemed of little importance as long as each instrument sounded to capacity.

As you can see by the illustrations the wedding chair is heavily embroidered and the attached poles are carried by a guild of men who make their living by such work. A mirror may have been placed in this wedding chair to frighten away the evil spirits that may be hidden in the corners, the idea being that if the spirits see themselves in the mirror they will be frightened away by their own reflections.

79

The bride is dressed at home in her red embroidered skirt, jacket and heavy red veil, and put into the chair by Sung Ch'in T'ai-Tai, a woman chosen by the family to bring good luck to the bride. The front flap of the chair is said to be fastened very securely so that there can be no exchanging of brides. It is told that once upon a time a suffocated bride arrived at the wedding feast because of the lack of ventilation in the tightly closed chair.

Before this time, the carriers come to take the household equipment and trousseau to the groom's house. This must have been what I ran into the first evening in Peiping. Uniformed carriers were going through the streets shouting something which I couldn't understand. There were many trays of folded silk gowns exposed to the wind and dust, trays of hair ornaments —jewels—"Missy boxes"—tables—bedding with the wash basin tied on the top, dishes, porcelain mugs, and from one carrier's shoulder pole dangled several empty Standard Oil cans, which, by the way, are very useful to the cooks of Peiping.

Perhaps the item which most aroused my curiosity was a crate containing live ducks and two live cackling geese of pinkish hue sticking their long necks through the slats of the crate. I could almost understand that language of the Wisconsin farm! This sending of live, highly-dyed geese, I learned later, is a very common practice and that almost all gifts are given in pairs.

The many carriers and the number of articles in this procession must have given the bride's family a great deal of prestige as it showed the people in the street that the daughter had been amply provided for by her family.

80

The groom kneels to meet the chair, lifts the bride out and carries her over to the doorway and the glowing charcoal fire which is burning there to foil any evil spirits which may be lurking around trying to gain entrance. The bride is carried over the threshold of the bridal chamber.

The groom lifts the veil and sees, for the first time, the girl his parents have chosen for him to marry. Two small cups of spirits, fastened together by a cord or tassel are given to the pair. They drink from these and exchange cups. After the cup ceremony the couple is served a specially prepared food of which the shy bride eats very little.

The couple now goes to kow-tow to the groom's parents and to his family.

During the feast which follows the new bride is either helping serve the parents and guests or has retired to the bridal chamber to receive the comments of the guests and family which sometimes are far from being kind or complimentary. The idea is to tease the bride. One tries to make her laugh. The impression the bride makes on the new family often dates from this teasing, and how she responds to it. Some say, later that night, after all the guests have departed, some of the groom's friends return, try to enter the house, and carry away something belonging to the groom, which the groom must later redeem at the price set upon it by the teasing friends.*

---

*I have never seen a Chinese Wedding, only the many colorful processions on the streets of Peiping. This account has been gleaned from books and from my Chinese friends. Not all weddings are of this traditional type.

Shuttlecock

Shuttlecock is a very popular game with Chinese children. One often becomes quite skilled in keeping the shuttlecock in the air by kicking it with his foot. (It is easier to kick if wearing the padded cloth Chinese shoe which is straight across the instep.)

The shuttlecock is made by tying feathers in the square hole of a cash. It is an easy and inexpensive toy to make which may account, to some degree, for its popularity.*

---

*Note how the artist's style has changed.

一個鍵　踢兩半兒
yi　ke　chien　t'i　liang　pan　erh

打花鼓　繞花線兒
ta　hua　ku　jao　hua　hsien　erh

裏踢外拐
li　t'i　wai　kuai

八仙過海
pa　hsien　kuo　hai

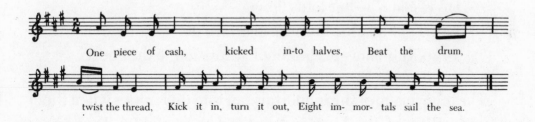

One piece of cash, kicked in-to halves, Beat the drum,

twist the thread, Kick it in, turn it out, Eight im- mor- tals sail the sea.

Shuttlecock

> One piece of cash, kicked into halves,
> Beat the drum, twist the thread,
> Kick it in, turn it out,
> Eight immortals sail the sea.

The reference here to the immortals crossing the sea tells of their visit to see the things in the sea and to attend the birthday party of Mother Wang, the Queen of the Fairies. They used their various special talents in transportation. They did not use ships but the following to help themselves:

> "Li T'ieh-Kuai—his crutch
> Chung-li Ch'uan—his feather fan
> Chang Kuo-lao—his paper mule
> Lü Tung pin—his sword
> Han Hsiang Tzu—her flower basket
> Ho Hsien Ku—her lotus flower
> Lan Ts'ai-ho—his musical instrument
> Ts'ao Kuo-chiu—his tablet of admission to the court"

The pilgrimage of the immortals ran into difficulties when the Dragon King of the Eastern Sea tried to steal Lan Ts'ai-ho's musical instrument. The immortals gave battle, came out victorious and continued on their way.

There are many stories about these eight immortals who were crossing the sea to go to the birthday party of Mother Wang, the Queen of the Fairies.

Some of these immortals, the fairies of happiness, (Pa Hsien) are said to have actually lived in the Sung Dynasty, while others are purely mythical. There are long and exciting tales about each one and how they happened to become immortal. No two reached immortality by the same path.

One often meets these fairies as decorations on panels, china-wear, borders, etc. Each one has a characteristic something in his hand which he always carries. It was this object which each fairy turned into a sea monster in order to cross the sea to the birthday party of Mother Wang. Here is a little information about the fairies so you can call them by name the next time you meet them.

Li T'ieh-Kuai always carries an iron crutch and a pouch of magic medicine. It is said that during his pilgrimages on earth he also carried a little glass bottle which, when sleepy, he would hang on the wall, and, by making himself small, he would have a place to sleep. The next morning he would come out of the bottle and continue on his way.

Lan Ts'ai-ho carries a flute and cymbals with which he entertains all the other immortals. As the fairies were crossing the sea to attend the birthday party of Mother Wang, the Dragon King of the Eastern Sea came out of his lair and tried to take the musical instrument away from Lan Ts'ai-ho. A great battle followed between the Dragon King and the Eight Immortals. Finally, the immortals won and continued on their way to the birthday party.

Chang Kuo-lao always rode a mule which became a piece of paper at the journey's end. Chang Kuo-lao had only to fold the paper up, and put it in his pocket. When he needed transportation for another journey he would take the paper out of his pocket, sprinkle water on it, and the mule would come to life again.

Lü Tung-pin was an excellent fencer, so he can be recognized by the sword which he carries. Once upon a time, so the legend says, Lü Tung-pin went through all the provinces selling oil to those who wanted to buy. He would make anyone immortal who did not ask for more than that which was being paid for. But, alas, alas, he found only one person—a little old lady. Later Lü Tung-pin returned to her house and by putting a few grains of rice into the well in her courtyard, he was able to change the water into wine. This, the old lady sold, and became very wealthy.

Han Hsiang Tzu always carries a flower basket filled with flowers which were grown on a very small bit of earth. Verses, written in gold letters can be seen on the leaves.

Ho Hsien Ku always carries a lotus flower and had a very interesting life before she became immortal and went to live in the realm of the fairies.

Ts'ao Kuo-chiu always carries his tablets of admission to the Imperial Court. When Ts'ao Kuo-chiu grew very old he became a hermit and lived by himself.

Chung-li Ch'uan always carried a feathered fan or the peach of immortality. His special ability was combining metals.*

---

*If you want to hear more about these eight immortals, your librarian can help you find books which will tell you the complete story.

Chinese Words and Phrases *

In the following pages you will find Chinese words, more properly called "characters." A character may be a word in itself or it may take several characters to form a word. The English equivalent is given on the right side of the Chinese character.

The sounds are generally pronounced as in the English language, with some slight variations. Some of these are as follows:

a, as the "a" in father	t', as the "t" in tell
e, as the "e" in let	k, almost as the "g" in gate
ê, as the German "ö"	k', as the "k" in kite
i, as the "i" in it	p, as the "p" in spot (almost as b)
o, as the "o" in hole	p', as the "p" in pot
u, as the "oo" in wood	ao, as the "ou" in ouch
u, as the "u" in cut	ai, as the "ai" in Port Said
t, as the "t" in stay (almost as d)	hs, as the "sh" in shoe (somewhat softer)

---

*This information on the Chinese language is included at the suggestion of Anne Fenwick Britton and John Seacord, the Little Carps, who wanted to learn a few Chinese characters. On looking over the galley proof Anne thought it would be fun to be able to say a few words in Chinese and to write just one character so a Chinese person would recognize it. With the help of Dr. Yun Hsia, you, Anne, will now be able to write *many* characters and to build acceptable sentences in no time at all. Dr. Hsia has outlined some play material on the Chinese language which will enable you, in five minutes, to read and write some Chinese. 'Tis true the sentences will be very simple, but nevertheless they will be acceptable Chinese anywhere in China, as the meaning of the written characters is the same all over China. Various provinces, or what we might call states, will give different tones, inflections or pronunciations to the character. This leads one to believe that each province speaks a different language. This is rather untrue. We have similar variations in English speech within the boundaries of this country, although it perhaps is not as marked. But first, before you and your playmates start to find the characters which fill the squares, and to build similar sentences of your own, will you please read what Dr. Hsia suggested I tell you:

"To master the Chinese language is a big order (some scholars spend a lifetime on language study and still have more to learn at the age of 101), but it is not as difficult as people usually think, if one is determined to learn it. For serious study of the language you must consult a standard text book."

The pronunciation used here follows the Wade system for romanization of Mandarin, the official Chinese "dialect." Each character has a definite tone which must be pronounced exactly right in order to speak good Chinese. These tonal changes are four in number and are as follows:

NUMBER		CHARACTERISTICS
1	——	even
2	╱	going up slightly (as if asking a question)
3	╲╱	going down, then up
4	╲	going down, or fading out

Try the four tones for *Ma*, remembering the "a" is pronounced as the "a" in father. Each tone will give you a different Chinese character, written differently and meaning a different thing.

For the most part, the sentence structure is about the same as that of English, i.e.:

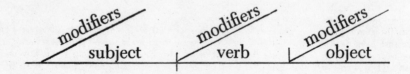

One rule is that all modifiers must precede the part modified. For instance:

English order—I saw the man from China again today.
Chinese order—I today again saw the from China man.

In asking a question the verb or adjective is repeated, e.g.:

Good not good?   hao pu hao
(Is it all right?)

Come not come?   lai pu lai
(Are you coming?)

(There is no change of form in the verbs through the person, tense, gender or number.)

You can select characters from the following pages and make sentences of your own.

The characters are written with a Chinese pen which is like an artist's brush. The rhymes in the text are written with an ordinary fountain pen. This latter is now one accepted way of writing Chinese. Usually the Chinese is written in vertical columns from top to bottom, with the columns going from right to left. It is also correct to write horizontally, as you see in the text of this book. It is like the English which reads in lines from left to right.

Do not be afraid to experiment with the writing of Chinese characters. You do not need a brush. Use your pencil to make the lines. As long as you have the necessary strokes in the character, it is complete and can be read by any Chinese. Try it. Write a letter to your friend in Chinese. It is fun.

WORDS, MANY OF WHICH ARE MADE OF ONE CHARACTER

ADJECTIVES, ADVERBS AND PREPOSITIONS

好 (hao³) good	紅 (hung²) red	上 (shang⁴) up	快 (k'uai⁴) quick
壞 (huai⁴) bad	綠 (lü⁴) green	下 (hsia⁴) down	慢 (man⁴) slow
美 (mei³) beautiful	黃 (huang²) yellow	左 (tso³) left	前 (ch'ien²) front
大 (ta⁴) large	藍 (lan²) blue	右 (yu⁴) right	後 (hou⁴) hind
小 (hsiao³) small	黑 (hei¹) black	中 (chung¹) middle center	從 (ts'ung²) from
多 (to¹) many much	白 (pai²) white	不 (pu⁴) not	到 (tao⁴) to
少 (shao³) few	方 (fang¹) square	很 (hên³) very	回 (hui²) (come) back
香 (hsiang¹) fragrant	圓 (yüan²) round	同 (t'ung²) with	又 (yu⁴) again

90

球 (ch'iu²) ball	春 (ch'un¹) spring	糖 (t'ang²) candy	山 (shan¹) hill
花 (hua¹) flowers	夏 (hsia⁴) summer	餅 (ping³) cake	水 (shui³) water
茶 (ch'a²) tea	秋 (ch'iu¹) autumn	果 (kuo³) fruit	石 (shih²) stone
樹 (shu⁴) tree	冬 (tung¹) winter	菜 (ts'ai⁴) vege-table	河 (hê²) river
草 (ts'ao³) grass	東 (tung¹) east	人 (jên²) man	車 (ch'ê¹) car
家 (chia¹) home	西 (hsi¹) west	狗 (kou³) dog	衣 (yi¹) clothes
門 (men²) door	南 (nan²) south	貓 (mao¹) cat	鞋 (hsieh²) shoes
牆 (ch'iang²) wall	北 (pei³) north	羊 (yang²) goat	帽 (mao⁴) hat

來 (lai²) come

去 (ch'ü⁴) go

走 (tsou³) walk

跑 (p'ao³) run

跳 (tiao⁴) jump

睡 (shui⁴) sleep

開 (k'ai¹) open

關 (kuan¹) close

吃 (ch'ih¹) eat

喝 (hê¹) drink

寫 (hsieh³) write

讀 (tu²) read

畫 (hua⁴) draw

學 (hsüeh²) learn

說 (shuo¹) speak

打 (ta³) play (ball)

看 (k'an⁴) see

聽 (t'ing¹) hear

站 (chan⁴) stand

坐 (tso⁴) sit

愛 (ai⁴) love

要 (yao⁴) want

是 (shih⁴) be (is, am, are)

有 (yu³) have

飛 (fei¹) fly

叫 (chiao⁴) cry call

笑 (hsiao⁴) smile laugh

買 (mai³) buy

賣 (mai⁴) sell

拿 (na²) bring take

推 (t'ui¹) push

拉 (la¹) pull

CARDINALS	ORDINALS	MONTHS	WEEK DAYS
一 (i¹) 1	第一 (ti⁴ i¹) 1st	一月 (i¹ yüeh⁴) January	禮拜一 (li³ pai⁴ i¹) Monday
二 (erh⁴) 2	第二 (ti⁴ erh⁴) 2nd	二月 (erh⁴ yüeh⁴) February	禮拜二 (li³ pai⁴ erh²) Tuesday
三 (san¹) 3	第三 (ti⁴ san¹) 3rd	三月 (san¹ yüeh⁴) March	禮拜三 (li³ pai⁴ san¹) Wednesday
四 (ssu⁴) 4	第四 (ti⁴ ssu⁴) 4th	四月 (ssu⁴ yüeh⁴) April	禮拜四 (li³ pai⁴ ssu⁴) Thursday
五 (wu³) 5	第五 (ti⁴ wu³) 5th	五月 (wu³ yüeh⁴) May	禮拜五 (li³ pai⁴ wu³) Friday
六 (liu⁴) 6	第六 (ti⁴ liu⁴) 6th	六月 (liu⁴ yüeh⁴) June	禮拜六 (li³ pai⁴ liu⁴) Saturday
七 (ch'i¹) 7	第七 (ti⁴ ch'i¹) 7th	七月 (ch'i¹ yüeh⁴) July	禮拜日 (li³ pai⁴ jih⁴) Sunday
八 (pa¹) 8	第八 (ti⁴ pa¹) 8th	八月 (pa¹ yüeh⁴) August	
九 (chiu³) 9	第九 (ti⁴ chiu³) 9th	九月 (chiu³ yüeh⁴) September	早上 (tsao³ shang⁴) morning
十 (shih²) 10	第十 (ti⁴ shih²) 10th	十月 (shih² yüeh⁴) October	中午 (chung¹ wu³) noon
十一 (shih² i¹) 11	第十一 (ti⁴ shih² i¹) 11th	十一月 (shih² i¹ yüeh⁴) November	晚上 (wan³ shang⁴) evening
十二 (shih² erh⁴) 12	第十二 (ti⁴ shih² erh⁴) 12th	十二月 (shih² erh⁴ yüeh⁴) December	下午 (hsia⁴ wu³) forenoon
			上午 (shang⁴ wu³) afternoon

93

我 (wo³) I 　　我們 (wo³men¹) we 　　我的 (wo³ ti⁴) my mine 　　我們的 (wo³ men¹ ti⁴) our, ours

你 (ni³) you 　　你們 (ni³ men¹) you 　　你的 (ni³ ti⁴) your yours 　　你們的 (ni³ men¹ ti⁴) your, yours

他 (t'a¹) He, she, it 　　他們 (t'a¹ men¹) they 　　他的 (t'a¹ ti⁴) his, her, its 　　他們的 (t'a¹ men¹ ti⁴) their, theirs

這 (chê⁴) this
那 (na⁴) that
父親 (fu⁴ ch'in²) father
母親 (mu³ ch'in¹) mother
哥哥 (kê¹ kê¹) elder brothers
姐姐 (çhieh³ chieh³) elder sister
弟弟 (ti⁴ ti⁴) younger brother
妹妹 (mei⁴ mei⁴) younger sister
朋友 (p'êng² yu³) friends
早 (tsao³) (good) morning

這些 (chê⁴ hsieh¹) these
那些 (na⁴ hsieh¹) those
這裡 (chê⁴ li³) here
那裡 (na⁴ li³) there
那裡 (na² li³) where
什麼 (shen² ma¹) what
怎樣 (tsên³ yang⁴) how
謝謝 (hsieh⁴ hsieh⁴) thanks
再見 (tsai⁴ chien⁴) good bye
前天 (ch'ien² t'ien¹) day before yesterday
後天 (hou⁴ t'ien¹) day after tomorrow

姓 (hsing⁴) surname
名字 (ming² tzu⁴) name
中國 (chung¹ kuo²) China
中國人 (chung¹ kuo² jen²) Chinese people
中國話 (chung¹ kuo² hua⁴) Chinese language
美國 (mei³ kuo²) U. S. A.
美國人 (mei³ kuo² jen²) Americans
今天 (chin¹ t'ien¹) today
明天 (ming² t'ien¹) tomorrow
昨天 (tso² t'ien¹) yesterday

您好嗎 (nin² hao³ ma¹) how are you?
對不起 (tui⁴ pu⁴ ch'i³) I beg your pardon.
甭客氣 (pêng² k'ê⁴ ch'i⁴) Don't mention it.
今天天氣好 (chin¹ t'ien¹ t'ien¹ ch'i⁴ hao³) The weather is fine today.

94

Example:

English:

Chinese Characters:

She is my younger sister

☐ ☐ ☐─ ☐─

Chinese Pronunciation
  in Wade Romanization:

T'a¹ shih⁴ wo³-ti⁴ mei⁴-mei⁴

Literal translation:

She is my younger sister

1 — What   is   her   name?

☐ ☐ ☐─ ☐─

T'a¹   chiao⁴   shen²-ma¹   ming²-tzu⁴

She called   what   name?

2 — Her   name   is   __ __ __ __

☐ ☐

T'a¹   chiao⁴

She   called   __ __ __ __ __

3 — This   is   my   puppy.

☐ ☐ ☐─ ☐─

Chê⁴   shih⁴   wo³-ti⁴   hsiao²-kou³.

This   is   my   little   dog.

95

4 – I love my puppy.

☐ ☐ ☐– ☐–

Wo³ ai⁴ wo³ti⁴ hsiao²-kou³.

I love my little dog.

5 – He comes home with me.

☐ ☐ ☐ ☐ ☐ ☐

T'a¹ t'ung² wo³ hui² chia¹ lai².

He with me back home come.

6 – Do you drink tea?

☐ ☐ ☐ ☐ ☐

Ni³ hê¹ pu⁴ hê¹ ch'a²

You drink not drink tea?

7 – I do not drink tea; I drink water.

☐ ☐ ☐ ☐ ☐ ☐ ☐

Wo³ pu⁴ he¹ ch'a² wo³ hê¹ shui³.

I not drink tea, I drink water.